bang on the door™ ©

top dj

groovy chick's diaries

(almost) private

School Holidays

Whoopee!

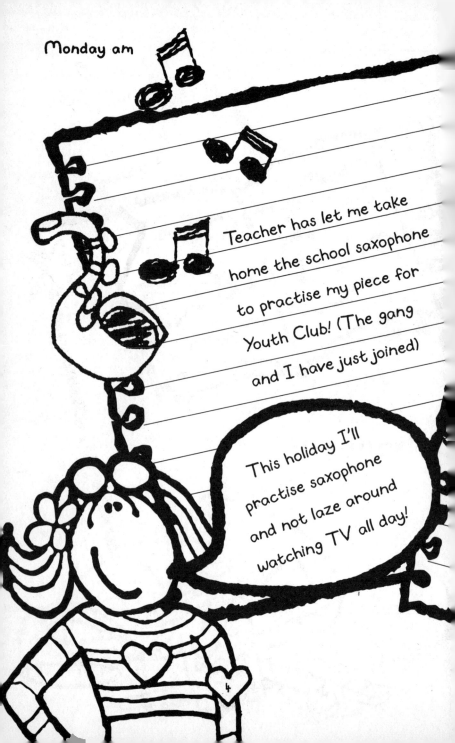

Youth Club
is sooo
cool!

We do loads of
fun things!

Just off to funky girl's
to pick out fab CDs to
take there on Friday.

CD

CD

CD

5

Tuesday am

h-o-o-o-w-l-l-l-l

Practised saxophone piece over and over. My dog howled so much, Mum took him for a walk. Said she needed to get out the house — wonder why?

6

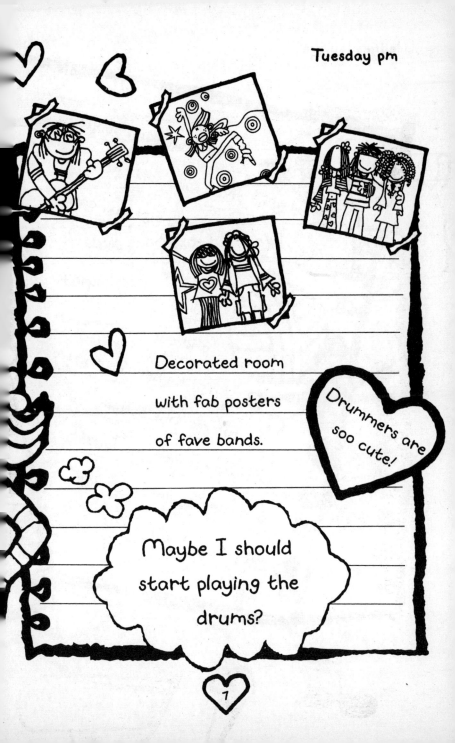

Decorated room
with fab posters
of fave bands.

Drummers are soo cute!

Maybe I should start playing the drums?

Told my mum I was thinking about learning to drum. She said there are more peaceful things you can do with two sticks!

Mum went shopping and came home with knitting needles and wool for me. She bought earplugs for her and Dad! Bet famous singers' mums never did that!

Thursday am

Fave kind of moring...

Reading, eating sweets

and sorting make-up.

1pm: **Funky girl** over

for lunch.

What a scream!

Funky girl and I tried out

truly bizarre clothes combos.

It was a totally cool evening, but the best bit was when our Youth Club Leader pinned up this notice!

Yay!

Attention Members!

Due to popular demand Youth Club will be open during school holidays daily, from 10am – 8pm.

Youth Club Leader

Cleaned up room so there

was space for sleeping bags.

Made fave fizzy

drinks for friends.

Yum!

fizz

Groovy sleepover with my friends. Made popcorn and sang songs. Drooled over pictures of fave bands. Talked and talked about truly fab news that Youth Club will be open during school holidays. Told jokes about things we will do... Giggled all night 'til my mum told us to settle down.

Had groovy morning trying on clothes. We made a catwalk out of the hallway.

Then we had a mad fashion parade with all the best outfits.

Totally cool!

16

Mum made us a brilliant tea with cakes and sandwiches.

Scrummy!

Youth Club tomorrow. Yes!

Don't you just love sleepovers!

17

Week

Sooooooo cool hanging out at the Youth Club.

There are a zillion fantastic things to do, like listening to music, having a laugh, chilling out, gossiping and telling stories.

Groovy Youth Club Leader

And Youth Club Leader wants suggestions for more!

How cool is that?!

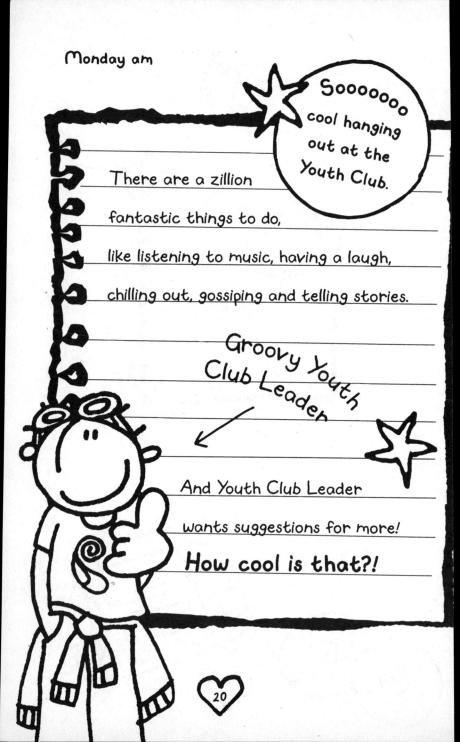

20

Youth Club gets better...

Great to see all my friends. Made wicked club badges, played games and told jokes.

Q. Why did the chicken cross the road?
A. Because it was the frog's day off.

Q. What do you call a boy with one foot on the bus?
A. Justin.

Q. Did anyone laugh when you fell on the ice?
A. No but the ice made a few cracks.

Q. What's a good way to keep a bus warm?
A. Put a coat of paint on it.

Ha! Ha! Hee! Hee!

22

Brill idea!

We're going to paint pictures on the walls of the Youth Club! Me and my mates will do one side, boys will do the other.

Wednesday am

Got to Youth Club early to start painting.

We put some music on

as we painted.

It was sooo cool!

Pop princess got so carried away with showing us her funky moves that she stepped in a can of paint! Youth Club Leader was really cool about it. Just said we would have to paint the floor too!

Played my saxophone piece to Youth Club.

Was sooo nervous.

Only missed top notes (sounded more like a rude noise!). Some of the boys laughed but they clapped like mad when I finished.

(Whew!)

Glad it's all over.

Mum said she is too

and my dog just took one look

at the saxophone and ran off

whining, with his tail between

his legs.

27

Fabulous feast
at club today.
We all brought something.

Cakes

Hot dogs

Fizzy drinks

Cheese sandwiches

Deeelish!

We shared it around and told

funny stories. Then we made

leaflets asking for donations of used

games and computer stuff for Youth

Club. It was raining outside but it was

cosy and warm in the Youth Club.

Really cool day!

Saturday am

Got up early to go roller
blading with **funky girl**, pop princess
and **roller babe**.

Wicked!

Pheew!

All that blading has made me really tired. Only two hours to go 'til disco at Youth Club.

Time for a fruity face pack and a soak in the tub with lots of strawberry bath foam!

31

Dreamed of fab disco at Club last night. **Groovy guy** picked out totally cool CDs and we danced ourselves silly!

Lazed about all day nibbling

on scrummy chocolate. Can't

work out whether I like

dark choc or milk kind

the best. I'll have

to keep testing

until I can decide.

Mmmmmm!

Oooops! I think I feel

a teeny weeny bit sick!

Week

The Week the Youth Clu

Three

Got A Surprise Gift

Most amazingly fab thing!

Just can't believe it!

Dj babe's brother's Rock Club has donated two groovy turntables, two blasting loud speakers and a totally cool mixer, used, but **fab!**

We are going to practise scratching and mixing sounds!

(Like real DJs!)

36

We are all so excited, especially since Mum says she'll give us all her old 70's and 80's records!

Aren't mums the coolest?

We spent all day setting up the sound system. We put the mixer in the middle of the two decks, and then connected them with the wires (Youth Club Leader did all the electric bits). Then we added the two speakers at either side.

It looked really cool and there was a huge sound!

38

Funky girl gave us a set of her Dad's headphones so we could be like real DJs and listen to what we were mixing.

Can't wait to get DJing!

Wednesday am

We got a quick lesson in how to DJ this morning... Youth Club Leader showed us how to work two turntables with records. When the records were playing together he faded the sound out from one of them, to get a groovy new sound!

He also showed us how to scratch records by moving them back and forth with his fingers. This made a cool rap sound!

We all took a turn on the decks (cool DJ speak for sound system). We need a lot more practise!

DJ babe made up a fab quiz to find out if we were Top DJs...

The bass is too loud. Do you:
a) Turn up the vocals?
b) Turn it down?
c) Cover your ears?

You have a cold. Do you:
a) DJ – a husky voice sounds cool?
b) Stay in bed?
c) Take your cough medicine with you?

Your mum says you're too young to go to the school disco. Do you:
a) Get your mates round for a party?
b) Sulk?
c) Sneak out and go anyway?

Practised my

DJing this morning.

I mixed the records,

changing the beat

and fading one record

into another.

Pop princess didn't seem too

impressed but her efforts

weren't much better!

Spent the afternoon practising cool DJ walk.

Ended up falling over own feet.

Not very groovy.

I am a Top DJ!

Saturday am

Was very tired

after all that

practising.

Watched telly with Mum 'n' Dad.

Cool documentary about being a DJ.

All the best DJs
practised loads!

Pheew!

47

Tried on loads of outfits to find coolest DJ look.

Pop princess sent me a text saying that Youth Club will be closed down.

:(Yth Clb 2 B closed!!

I don't believe it!

48

I knew music was
my destiny, but Dad
says it wasn't the
saxophone.

Back to school
tomorrow.

49

Week

The Week They Closed Our

Monday pm

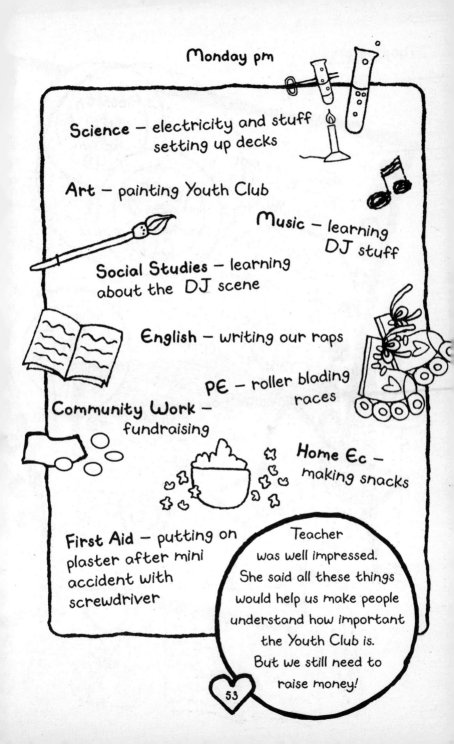

Science — electricity and stuff
setting up decks

Art — painting Youth Club

Music — learning
DJ stuff

Social Studies — learning
about the DJ scene

English — writing our raps

PE — roller blading
races

Community Work —
fundraising

Home Ec —
making snacks

First Aid — putting on
plaster after mini
accident with
screwdriver

Teacher
was well impressed.
She said all these things
would help us make people
understand how important
the Youth Club is.
But we still need to
raise money!

53

Everyone wore their Youth Club badges to show how much we miss it. Teacher said she would see what she could do to help!

Teachers are totally brill!

Fantabulous idea!

A DJ battle (competition to find the best DJ) to raise money!

Competitors:
dj babe
vibemaster
pop princess
dj dude
groovy guy
funky girl
me!

It would be so cool if we could raise enough to save our club!

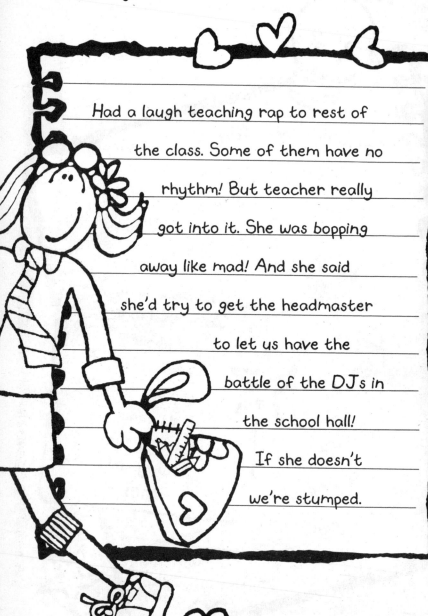

Had a laugh teaching rap to rest of the class. Some of them have no rhythm! But teacher really got into it. She was bopping away like mad! And she said she'd try to get the headmaster to let us have the battle of the DJs in the school hall! If she doesn't we're stumped.

Two of the music shop guys were so totally cool, that they offered to help out our Youth Club with the battle of the DJs.

How kind is that?

58

After school funky
girl and I went through the cool
gear I bought in the music shop.
My favourite was the funky
top with heart; she liked the
cool, baggy trousers.

We really look like
Top DJs now!

59

Friday am

Great News!

Headmaster came into classroom in the middle of maths and he and our teacher went into huddle, nodding and whispering. Teacher told us to put down our pens and pencils. It was well exciting.

Then she gave us the news...

We can use the school hall for the battle of the DJs!

We were all dead excited!

The whole class cheered.

Headmasters aren't that bad after all!

Hooray! Yay! Hooray!

Yay! Yay!

61

Our first practise
in the school
hall was fab!

The music shop guys came and

helped us set up. They know

sooo much!

Chuckle fest when **funky girl** tried some scratching on the decks. It sounded more like a cat pawing the records. Practising for the battle of the DJs is wicked. Tomorrow is the boys' turn on the decks.

Some of the boys are really good. Was being fair and said we'd have to really practise to beat them. Then dj dude said girls couldn't be DJs!

Girls can't be DJs!

Cheek!

64

I'll show him!

Groovy chick is one Top DJ who wont be beat.

Us girls said we would

practise even harder!

Week

The Week We
For

We can practise in the hall after school for one hour.

Contestants for battle of the DJs get 10 minutes to practise on the decks. Not enough, but better than nothing.

In art we designed posters for the competition.

Here is my fave.

Tuesday am

list

Planning a battle

of the DJs takes lots

of organisation.

Made a list to make sure we didn't

forget anything.

battle of the DJs!
from *groovy chick & friends*
to: *everybody!*
place: *school hall*
date & time: *monday! 8.00pm*

Practise moves
Learn rap
Invitations
Decorate school hall
Organise nibbles
Practise mixing
Shop for outfit
Follow beauty regime

eyemask

Wheew!

All that list-making has

made me tired!

Think I'll have a rest

this evening and

get busy tomorrow.

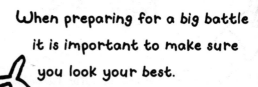

When preparing for a big battle it is important to make sure you look your best.

We came up with these top tips to make sure we all look groovy on the big day!

Get lots of exercise — makes you feel good, and is good for your complexion.

Choose your shoes carefully — broken ankles are not cool!

Wear comfortable clothes — it's easy to look good when you're comfy.

Rub in moisturiser
— stops the hot
lights drying out
your skin.

Put some glitter in
your hair — will sparkle
under the lights.

hair gel

Get plenty of sleep —
being rested helps
you concentrate.

Always smile —
happy faces are
much prettier
than frowny ones!

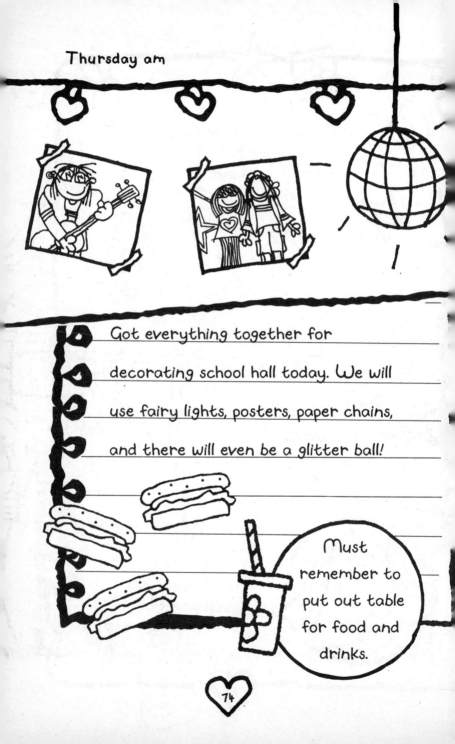

Got everything together for decorating school hall today. We will use fairy lights, posters, paper chains, and there will even be a glitter ball!

Must remember to put out table for food and drinks.

More battle practise.

Did poptastic moves, rapping,

mixing and scratching.

Top tip from music shop guys...

Keep head up (except when

scratching!). And keep smiling!

75

Couldn't get to sleep last night.

Kept practising my rap

over and over in head.

Finally dropped off and

dreamed about winning

battle. Was holding first

prize and everybody

was cheering!

yay!

hooray!

Had long soak in
lavender scented bath
tonight to try and relax.

Hope I have **another** great
dream about winning battle.
And saving the Youth Club!

lavender

We spent all day practising and making

tickets for the battle of the DJs.

Our headmaster was the best!

He saw us working away

writing out each ticket and

he took the best one and made

photocopies of it!

It saved loads of time!

battle of the DJs!

from: groovy chick & friends

to: everybody!

place: school hall

date & time: monday! 8.00pm

Mum 'n' Dad bought six tickets. They are going to bring **their** mums and dads!

Sooo embarrassing!

Wish the dog could come too!

Sunday am

Spent all day decorating school hall
and setting up sound system.

It looks so cool!

After that it's all systems
go in the kitchen with fab
and funky food.

How cool is that?

The ultimate popping party
drink – fizzy sherbet lemonade!

Snackalicious goodies to
get those tastebuds jumping!

Yum!

Week

The Week We Battled

Six

Monday am

Tonight's the night! I'm **sooo** nervous.

A luxurious soak in calming lavender bubble bath is the answer.

hair gel

Gave my hair a lemon conditioner to bring out the highlights, then sprinkled it with glitter to sparkle in the spotlight.

A shimmery manicure with daisy nail stickers will get fingertips noticed on the turntables.

Crystal gel over face and shoulders to complete the look.

We were all **really** nervous before the competition started.

Pop princess forgot her records and dj babe tripped over some wires on her way to the stage.

The hall was really packed out, everybody's family and friends were there to cheer them on. Even the music shop guys had brought their friends.

87

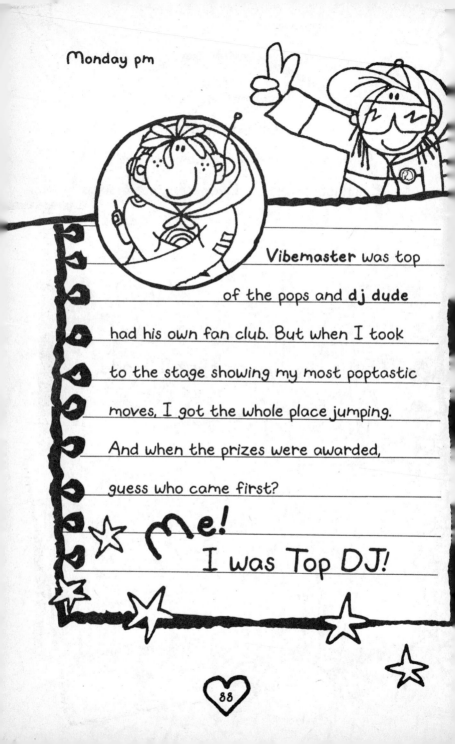

Vibemaster was top of the pops and **dj dude** had his own fan club. But when I took to the stage showing my most poptastic moves, I got the whole place jumping. And when the prizes were awarded, guess who came first?

me!

I was Top DJ!

This is the speech that I made:

"I'd like to thank my Mum 'n' Dad, the music shop guys for all their help, our teacher for getting us the lovely hall and the fab Rock Club for their gift of the sound system. Most of all the school, for helping us to raise the funds to save our Youth Club!"

Here is my Top DJ rap:

I'm a Top DJ,

That ain't no lie!

I'm in the groove,

Lemme tell you why...

I play cool sounds,

Soul, funk and pop!

Hip hop and disco,

The music don't stop!

90

My jazz sounds rock,

The beat is jumpin'!

My reggae's cool,

It's really somethin'!

So if fun's your game,

Here's what I say...

Gimme a call,

'Cos I'm a Top DJ!

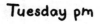
Tuesday pm

Youth Club Leader
has just given us the
great news!

We raised **over £800**

and the important people

at the council are so impressed with

that, plus all our mega skills, they are

re-opening the Youth Club!

The music shop guys enjoyed helping us

so much they want to join! So we've

made a whole lot of new friends!

It's groovy being a Top DJ!

more groovy reading!

bang on the door™©

Groovy Chick's Diaries 1:
Groovy Chick Hollywood Star
0-00-717636-8

It's just another day of fashion and fun
for **groovy chick** and until she has a fabulous
idea! She will have a Hollywood style party,
but will everything go as planned or will it
turn out to be more like a disaster movie?

Groovy Chick's Diaries 2:
In The Wild
0-00-717637-6

The summer holidays are finally here
and **groovy chick's** off to summer camp!
Who will be camp diva and what can she
wear to the disco?
Get out and about and go wild with
your favourite groovy girly.

Groovy Chick's Diaries 4:
Circus Crazy
0-00-717641-4   6/9/2004
Swing into action with the one and
only **groovy chick** and friends!
Groovy chick goes circus crazy, but can
she master her big top skills in time
to amaze everyone?

First published in Great Britain by
HarperCollins Children's Books in 2004

1 3 5 7 9 10 8 6 4 2
ISBN: 0 00 717638 4

Bang on the door character copyright:
© 2004 Bang on the Door all rights reserved.
⊕ bang on the door®© is a trademark
Exclusive right to license by Santoro
www.bangonthedoor.com

The HarperCollins website address is:
www.harpercollinschildrensbooks.co.uk